Creating the body y[...]

basic
exercises
vol. 1

Calasanz Martial Arts System

Creating The Body You Want

Written by
Calasanz & Cathy Cash Spellman

Designed by
Anthony Esposito

Photography by
Jim Herity

Edited by
Grace A. Luppino

Graphics by
Tom Brenner

Produced by
Adam House, Wilton, CT

Printed in the USA. ISBN 0-9704623-0-1

9 8 7 6 5 4 3 2 1
Digit on right indicates the number of this printing.

Calasanz Martial Arts Publishing
507 Westport Avenue, Norwalk, CT 06851
1-800-414-9544   www.calasanz.com

Create *the body you want.*

Develop *mind and spirit.*

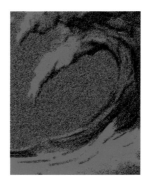

Train in the Calasanz System of martial arts.

The Chinese say

we receive our Shen/Spirit

as we enter the world of Light and Consciousness.

Spirit, in great measure, determines our destiny.

The Martial Arts

The name alone conjures legends ... of tapping ancient secrets to hone body, mind and spirit into balance ... of making super-human feats possible ... of harnessing chi, the lifeforce of the Universe.

Can these legends be true? And can this truth empower your life? Calasanz invites you to come with him on a grand journey of self discovery.

It is said by the sages that to learn Martial Arts is to dance with the Azure Dragon. Courage, grace, agility and mental fortitude will be demanded of you. Body, mind and heart will be expanded beyond previous boundaries. On this journey you will stretch your limits, lose your fear, and find the greatest of allies ... yourself.

The Calasanz Story

Calasanz is a Martial Arts Master who has spent a lifetime studying and teaching Karate, Kung Fu and Kickboxing. He has combined not only his Martial Arts mastery, but his training in ballet, gymnastics, weight and fitness counseling, into an absolutely unique system that has the capacity to help you create the body you've always dreamed of possessing, while it trains your mind and spirit to excel.

Calasanz has, for twenty years, trained young and old, professional athletes and dancers, law enforcement officers and a host of individuals from all walks of life in the Way of the Serene Warrior ... a way that leads to fitness, focus, health, strength and longevity.

The Power To Transform

Renowned as a hero in his native Dominican Republic, Calasanz firmly believes we all have the power to transform our lives, if we're willing to commit ourselves to the process.

"The integration of mind, body and spirit does not come from throwing yourself into grueling training sessions that cause burnout. Rather, it develops over time, as you patiently make your way through discipline, focus and determined work. I will teach you to reach deep inside yourself to master each new level. More patience and more inner strength are necessary to reach each successive goal. As you develop greater and greater martial arts maturity, instead of seeing a kick or a punch, you will see a way of life. You will become more patient in your work and home environment ... more self-confident ... you will develop the perseverance to achieve your highest goals in life. This is true transformation."

THE ENERGY WHICH ANIMATES ALL LIFE

... THE UNIVERSAL BREATH WHICH

GIVES US OUR EXISTENCE IS CALLED CHI.

When energies of the
body, mind and spirit are balanced,
tranquility prevails.

Perfect Body Conditioning ... for Martial Arts ... for life

This workbook is conceived to help you train in the most effective and practical way. While the movements and postures appear simple, they are actually sophisticated methods for the gradual creation of the agile, strong and elegant body you wish to achieve. This goal-oriented workbook is designed to lie flat on the floor beside you, to guide you step-by-step on your journey into health, fitness, enjoyment and physical mastery.

The secret to achieving your goal is to set a pace that keeps you motivated without causing burnout.

The Calasanz System uses ancient Chinese Martial Arts secrets, enhanced by modern isometric science, to help you become the best you can be, quickly enough so you are motivated by results you never dreamed possible.

If you are seeking to expand your warrior skills, your health, your fitness, your self confidence or your ability to defend yourself ... or if you're simply hoping to explore the many dimensions of your own being ... we welcome you to the shared path. As the ancient Chinese sages tell us, the journey of 1000 miles begins with a single step.

Welcome to the Journey

Lao-Tzu has said the Way

is not merely a course of action,

but the path to enlightenment.

The Calasanz Conditioning System

The Calasanz Karate & Kung-Fu System is a truly unique method of martial arts training. The stretching exercises in this book incorporate martial arts techniques intended to strengthen and elongate your muscles. They stress flexibility, body conditioning and safety.

Calasanz has spent years training with many of the world's great masters. He has gone beyond his traditional martial arts training to create techniques that work for the modern day martial arts student. Fifty percent of his student body are women - primarily interested in developing a strong, well toned body as well as practical self-defense techniques.

Modern Science ...
Ancient Knowledge

Calasanz's twenty years of training techniques have benefited hundreds of students of all ages. The effectiveness of his Aerobic Isolation and Isometrics system lies in the use of weight resistance in conjunction

with deep breathing, chi enhancing exercises and extension of the muscles. These exercises are performed in a slow and controlled manner in order to achieve the maximum benefit for the student, while at the same time avoiding injury.

The Calasanz System combines the use of weights, breathing, and slow, deliberate extension of the muscles, in order to develop flexibility, strength and endurance. This system not only helps students attain a high level of physical fitness, but also benefits them in training for self-defense and fighting. Age or a poor physique do not exclude anyone from the Calasanz System. These exercises are scientifically formulated to be performed by anyone regardless of their age or fitness level.

The Dojo

Calasanz Karate and Kung Fu Dojos are a revelation. With high rafters, punching bags, wrestling mats and regulation size boxing ring, they look like a place where machismo is the only order of business. Nothing could be further from the truth. The grunts and slaps and kiais - those powerful sounds martial artists use to boost the power of their chi - can be heard coming from a surprising variety of students - male and female, young and old, and every possible variation in between.

Calasanz himself spent years of training, not only in martial arts, but in dance, movement, gymnastics and sports, as well as philosophy. His training methods incorporate these varied disciplines and points of view into a unique system.

"I believe that if you can excite a student, he or she will love to learn," Calasanz explains. "You don't have to be a genius or a seasoned athlete to excel. All you need is the goal and the unshakable desire to make it come true."

The Calasanz System is right for you:

If you're searching for a way to
stay fit ... forever.

If you're an athlete wanting to be
the best you can be.

If you're searching for a sport
to fall in love with.

If you're intrigued by the history
and mystery of Martial Arts.

If you're looking for focus,
discipline and excellence.

Calasanz Karate & Kung Fu
can change your life!

Breath Equals Chi

Proper breathing is an essential component of the Calasanz Karate & Kung-Fu System. Every exercise begins with a deep inhalation and ends with a deep exhalation. You may have noticed that karate practitioners often yell or kiai when they execute a block or attack. This kiai is the result of a deep exhalation and is used for a variety of reasons. First, the kiai process draws oxygen into the body and releases toxins with each exhalation, providing the body with an enhanced supply of oxygen to prevent fatigue and promote mental alertness and endurance. Second, the kiai serves as a means of accumulating the powerful chi or internal force necessary to deliver a power charged technique. Finally, a loud kiai is also an effective psychological weapon used to intimidate the opponent. The kiai and the power behind it rely upon the martial artist's ability to produce chi.

What is Chi ?

Chi (Qi) is, quite simply, the energy of life. It's the central element of Chinese, and all Asian medicine, and it is the secret that empowers Martial Artists to do seemingly superhuman feats. What exactly is this Chi energy ... and how can you grasp it's reality enough to trust its vital importance to your life? The easiest analogy is the electricity that surrounds and lights up your life.

In order to visualize the mechanics of your body as a Martial Artist or Chinese physician would, imagine that you are not merely a physical being replete with flesh, bone, blood, fluid and assorted organs. Picture yourself, instead, as a three dimensional network of electrical circuitry. A glowing, pulsing, complex system of electrical impulses that hums with life-sustaining energy, which is constantly being transported to every centimeter of your being. That electrical energy is what we call lifeforce.

The Body Electric

Imagine that, like your computer or television set or microwave, there are large conductors and infinitesimal ones within you, each geared to perform a specific function. Like your appliances, you must be plugged into a source of power in order to function - your source is the electro-magnetic energy of the universe. Invisible waves of energy flow into you, through you, out of you, back to the source. The energy cannot be seen, any more than a radio wave or microwave can be seen by the naked eye. But the results are visible ... you are alive.

What is Chi used for?

Martial Artists master the use of their chi through specific movements and breathing techniques that were kept secret for centuries. These techniques are shown to students as they progress along the path toward mastery.

THE BASIC FLOOR EXERCISES

The floor exercises on the following pages begin the process of recreating your body. The body of a Martial Artist is not merely fit for combat and self-defense, it is fit for life.

The results you achieve will be limited only by your commitment and your intent.

Flexing Frog
Hip/Back Stretch

Calasanz has found that tightness in the hips, torso and pelvis often inhibits women's progress in the martial arts. Early in his career, Calasanz found that dance had a lot to offer a martial artist - poise, posture, fluidity - and he used this knowledge to develop a special training program for women. Therefore, he has incorporated dance movements and Wing Chun concepts into a unique series of exercises that target women's hip, torso and pelvic areas.

The Flexing Frog is superb for this purpose.

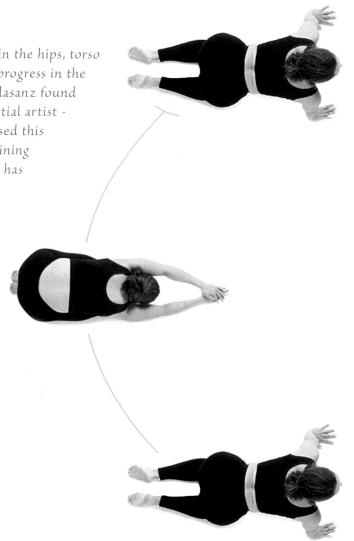

π firms up abdominals

π strengthens back

Step 1

Position yourself on your hands and knees - hands pointing forward.

Step 2

Inhale deeply and drop your buttocks onto your heels. Simultaneously drop your head and shoulders forward, with your arms extended out in front of you. Exhale.

Step 3

Return to the hands and knees position as in Step 1. You may arch your back for an added stretch. If you have back problems, keep your back flat.

Step 4

As you inhale deeply, drop back into a straddle position - knees spread as far apart as possible. If you are flexible enough and can drop further without straining, proceed to Step 5; if not, go to Step 7.

Flexing Frog

π *extends the entire pelvis*

Step 5
Drop a little further, pressing your hips into the ground while lowering yourself with your elbows. For a real challenge, go on to Step 6.

Step 6
If you are really flexible, drop your head and torso to the ground and rest your head on your elbows. Exhale as you settle into this stretch and remain in this position for about 10 seconds.

Step 7
Now inhale and draw your knees together. Return to the starting position - resting on your hands and knees. Repeat this exercise 10 times.

Flexing Frog

Gently round your back;
stretching the spine effortlessly.

You may arch your back for an added stretch.
If you have back problems,
keep your back flat.

Spread knees and stretch pelvis
with gradually increasing ease.

Dan Tien Power Crunch

Power Crunch

The Dan Tien Power Crunch loosens and strengthens the inner thigh muscles, improves leg flexibility, and builds up the pectoral and lower abdominal muscles. To execute this exercise, you will need a mat and a set of light dumbbells, no more than 2-5 pounds. Even if you are in reasonably good shape, do this exercise slowly and concentrate on form.

Step 1

Lie on your back on either a mat or carpet. Raise your arms and legs at a 90 degree angle. Your legs should be together, feet flexed, and your hands should be turned in with your palms (and dumbbells) facing each other.

Step 2

Simultaneously spread your arms and legs apart and inhale deeply. Your legs should drop as comfortably as possible. Drop your arms to your side. Slightly bend your elbows as you bring the weight down to avoid hyperextension.

π firms up abdominals

π strengthens back

π stretches the entire body

Step 3

In this position, tighten your lower
abdominal muscles and close your arms
and legs back into the starting position.
Exhale deeply. Perform 10 repetitions.

Dan Tien Power Crunch II

For a more challenging approach to this exercise,
you may wish to raise the legs at a 45 degree angle
instead of 90 degrees. Executing the exercise in this
position will increase the strength of the lower
abdominal muscles. You can also modify the angle
of the hands in order to work different portions of
the chest muscles. If you raise your arms higher
than shoulder level, be sure to use very light
weights in order to avoid injury.

Dan Tien Power Crunch

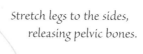

Stretch legs to the sides,
releasing pelvic bones.

Keep feet flexed.

Allow gravity to help
stretch legs downward and apart.

Samurai Sit-Up
Sit-Up Crunch

This challenging crunch works the upper
abdominals. A strong midsection is not
only essential to martial arts training,
but also increases the metabolism
so that the body burns more fat.
You will need a mat or carpet
and two light dumbbells.

π firms up abdominals

π strengthens back

π helps burn fat

Step 1
Lie on your back on either a mat or carpet. Your legs should be together, knees bent, while holding light dumbbells at the sides of your body.

Step 2
Simultaneously spread knees apart as you raise the dumbbells overhead. Inhale deeply. Your knees should drop as comfortably as possible. Slightly bend your elbows as you bring the weights overhead to avoid hyperextension. Your pelvis should be slightly arched, unless you have back problems. If so, keep back flat.

Step 3
In this position, tighten your upper abdominal muscles and raise your head and shoulders slightly off the floor. Simultaneously bring your arms and legs back to the starting position. Exhale deeply. Perform 10 repetitions.

Samurai Sit-Up

Keep lower abs tight.

Arch back and keep heels together.
If you have back problems, keep back flat.

Spirit Guardian
Side Kick Stretch

The side kick is one of the most powerful kicks in a martial artist's arsenal. The side kick is executed by thrusting the leg to the side of the body and striking the opponent with either the heel or the blade of the foot. This technique will help tone and stretch your muscles so that you may eventually perform this kick from a standing position.

Common targets for a standing side kick are the knee, inner thigh and midsection of your opponent's body. The ability to perform the side kick from this position is very useful if you are knocked to the ground in a self-defense situation.

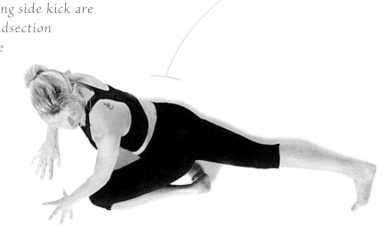

Step 1

Start by lying on your right side. Rest your body on your right arm and let your left arm drop along side as additional support. Draw your left knee in as close to your torso as possible and inhale. Your left foot should be resting on the ball of the foot with your heel pointing upwards.

Step 2

Extend your kick to the side of your body while dropping your torso down towards the floor. As you kick, isolate the muscles in your buttocks and use these muscles to push this kick outward. Note that the striking area of this kick is the heel. Make sure that the foot and ankle are tightly flexed as you extend your kick. This will train your hip, leg, foot and ankle to absorb the impact of striking an opponent. Exhale upon full extension of the kick.

Step 3
Draw your left knee back to the starting position. Repeat this exercise 10 times on each leg.

π strengthens thighs and calves

π develops powerful side kick

π trains foot and ankle to prepare for contact

Spirit Guardian

Use torque and pelvic strength to add power to your backward thrust.

Keep heel flexed in a combat position.

Surging Tiger
Back Kick

As you have seen in previous exercises, the Calasanz Stretching System incorporates martial arts movements. The back kick involves thrusting the leg backward and striking the opponent with the heel of the foot. Locking the hip upon impact is what makes this kick so powerful.

Step 1
Position yourself onto your hands and knees. Your hands are pointing forward. Arch your back, unless you have back problems. If so, keep back flat.

Step 2
Flex the left foot and lock it in the flexed position.

This exercise may be executed while wearing light ankle weights; but in the beginning, exercise without them. Once you are comfortable with the movements, you can start with 2 pound ankle weights and work your way up as your strength and flexibility permits.

π *increases pelvic strength*

π *strengthens back kicks*

Step 3

As you inhale deeply, drop down toward your right side so your head is lower than your torso. Lift your left leg backwards so that your thigh is parallel to your hip and left knee is bent.

Step 4

In this position, thrust the left leg backward. The foot should be flexed with the heel leading the thrust. As you execute this kick, exhale deeply. Do not hyperextend your kicking leg. Hold this position for a second or two. Now point the foot and flex it again.

Step 5

Return to the starting position. Repeat this exercise with the right leg. Alternate for 10 repetitions per leg.

Surging Tiger II

The Surging Tiger may also be executed from a different position. In Step 3, instead of dropping to the side before performing the exercise, drop forward. Deliver the kick from this position and alternate 10 kicks per leg. Notice your leg will not go as far back as it did in the previous exercise. This is the only variation; perform all the other steps in the Surging Tiger as outlined above.

Surging Tiger

Flex foot, thrust out and with heel locked.

Keep the back straight.

Keep the knee straight and foot flexed.

Celestial Stretch
Extended Stretch Sit-Up

The Calasanz System sit-up is unlike the traditional
sit-up in that the lower back is not strained. The
principles are the foundation of all Calasanz
System sit-ups - keeping the back rounded,
making long extended movements,
tensing the abdominal muscles,
and using weights and
momentum to propel
the body forward.

π firms up abdominals

π strengthens back

π stretches the entire body

Step 1
Sit in a leaning forward position with your legs extended; legs and feet together and toes comfortably pointing toward the ceiling. Place one dumbbell on each side of your legs. Grasp each weight with the corresponding hand and lean forward as much as you can until you feel a nice stretch. Your back should be rounded.

Step 2
While holding the dumbbells, inhale deeply. Now roll back while raising the dumbbells in front of you as far as you can without causing any strain in your shoulders. Arms should be kept straight at a comfortable angle; legs remain on the floor in the extended position.

Step 3
Remember, the roll back must be executed with a rounded back to avoid injury and the abdominal muscles must be tensed throughout this movement. As you slowly lower your body to the floor, exhale deeply, point your toes, and bring the weights up and back. Exhale as your body reaches the floor. You may arch your back for an added stretch once you've reached this position.

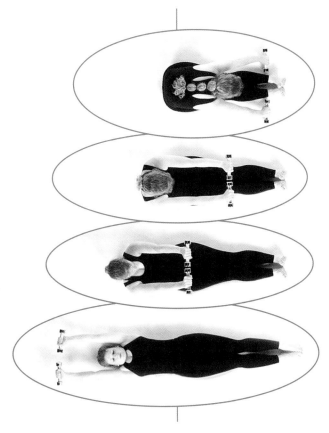

Step 4
You will now use a combination of momentum and the weight of the dumbbells to help you sit-up without straining your lower back. From a lying position, inhale deeply. With arms and dumbbells leading the way, sit up quickly. Keep stomach muscles tensed and lower back rounded on the way up.

Step 5
Roll up to the original starting position and lean forward for another stretch. Exhale. Repeat this exercise 10-15 times.

Celestial Stretch

Flex feet upward when
in the sitting position.

Keep abs tightened.

Point toes
when stretching out.

Jade Horse Straddle

Extended Straddle Stretch Sit-Up

This exercise is similar to the Celestial Stretch except that the legs are not extended in front of the body. In this technique, the legs are in a straddle position. The goal of this exercise is to stretch the hamstrings and improve flexibility.

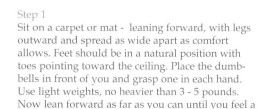

Step 1

Sit on a carpet or mat - leaning forward, with legs outward and spread as wide apart as comfort allows. Feet should be in a natural position with toes pointing toward the ceiling. Place the dumbbells in front of you and grasp one in each hand. Use light weights, no heavier than 3 - 5 pounds. Now lean forward as far as you can until you feel a nice stretch. Your back should be rounded.

π firms up abdominals

π improves flexibility

π stretches the hamstrings

Step 2

While holding the dumbbells, inhale deeply. Now tense your abdominal muscles and roll back while slowly raising the dumbbells.

Step 3

Continue rolling back slowly, as you make your way down to the floor. As you continue your roll back, continue raising the dumbbells in front of you as far as you can without causing strain in your shoulders. Arms should be kept straight, with a slight bend in your elbow to avoid hyperextension.

Depending on your strength and flexibility, you may not be able to extend your arms over your head. Keep an angle that is comfortable for you. Remember to keep your back rounded and tense your abdominal muscles.

Step 4

As you slowly lower your body to the floor, point your toes and bring the weights overhead as described in Step 3. Exhale as your torso and arms reach the floor. You may arch your back for an added stretch.

You will now use a combination of momentum, abdominal strength and the weight of the dumbbells to help you sit up without straining your lower back. From this lying position, inhale deeply. Tense your abdominal muscles. With arms and dumbbells leading the way, sit up briskly, allowing the weight of the dumbbells and strength of your abdominal muscles to propel you forward. Keep stomach muscles tensed and lower back rounded on the way up.

Step 5

Roll up to the starting position and lean forward for another stretch. Exhale. Repeat this exercise 10 - 15 times.

Jade Horse Straddle

Reach as far forward
as possible.

Stretch spine gently.

Breathe and be aware of abs.

Flapping Crane
Overall Body Exercise

This technique works the entire body, isolating the pectoral, inner thigh and abdominal muscles. In order to perform the Flapping Crane Exercise, you will need a mat or carpet and a set of dumbbells. Step Two of this exercise requires you to arch your back. If you have lower back problems, perform the exercise without the arch. Start off with light weights and work your way up as your strength improves.

π firms up abdominals

π strengthens thighs and pecs

π works the entire body

Step 1

Lie flat on your back. Grasp dumbbells and raise them over your chest at a 90 degree angle. Palms should be facing each other and dumbbells should be touching. Your knees should be bent and closed together. Your feet should be resting on your heels. Your back should be flat against the mat. Inhale deeply as you raise your arms and legs.

Step 2

Simultaneously drop your arms and knees to the sides of your body as you exhale. Arch your back on the way down unless you have back problems. Your arms should be in a 90 degree angle and resting at your sides. As you drop your knees, make sure you roll on your heels instead of your flat feet. This avoids strain on the knees.

Step 3

Now simultaneously lift the arms and knees to the starting position and inhale. As you pull up, contract your abdominal muscles and flatten your back. Perform 10 repetitions.

Flapping Crane II

The Flapping Crane works the pectoral muscles which will help firm the chest. A variation of this exercise will work the upper pectorals and the shoulder area. To exercise these different muscles, raise the dumbbells above your shoulders at a 45 degree angle. Whenever you raise your arms higher than shoulder level, be sure to use very light weights in order to avoid injury.

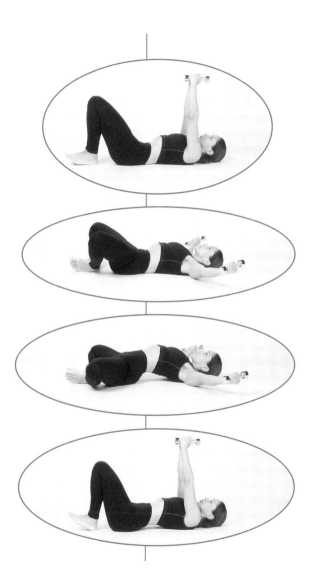

Flapping Crane

Feet together as knees drop toward the floor.

Knees and hands reach upward.

Work toward opening and stretching pelvis.

Double Dragon
Double Roundhouse Kick Stretch

The roundhouse kick is a versatile kick which can be executed as a power technique or in a quick jabbing motion. A low roundhouse kick aimed to side or back of the knee is an effective self-defense weapon. It requires strength, agility and timing; all of which are practiced in this exercise.

Step 1
Start this exercise by sitting on the floor. Your left leg is tucked closely in front of your body. Your right knee is bent in a hurdler's stretch, knee pointing straight forward. Inhale.

Step 2
Drop your torso and left arm to the left as you drop to the floor. Simultaneously, bring your right leg across your body. You may hold your leg with your right hand for support. Toes should be pointed and ankle tightened.

This exercise may be executed while wearing light ankle weights; but in the beginning, exercise without them. Once you are comfortable with the movements, you can start with 2 pound ankle weights and work your way up as your strength and flexibility permits.

π *strengthens leg muscles*

π *trains muscles for roundhouse kick*

Step 3
Slowly swing your right leg to the front of your body. The roundhouse kick is delivered in a hinging motion. Exhale as you extend the leg.

Step 4
Draw the right leg back across your body as you prepare to return to the starting position. Inhale deeply.

Step 5
Return your right leg to the starting position.

Step 6
In this position, gently twist your torso towards the right knee, feeling the stretch across your back. Exhale. Repeat this exercise 10 times on each leg.

Double Dragon

Turn body to
empower your kick.

Sit with back and
shoulders erect.

Torquing of leg
will provide thrust.

Double Dragon II
Double Roundhouse Kick Stretch

Because the roundhouse kick is versatile and can
be used in a variety of combat situations,
it's important to practice more than
one application of its potential
power. This variation increases
agility and reach.

Step 1
Start this exercise by sitting on the floor. Your left
leg is tucked closely in front of your body. The right
leg is bent in a hurdler's stretch, knee pointing
straight forward. Inhale.

Step 2
Drop your torso and left arm backwards.
Simultaneously, bring your right leg up and rest on
your hip. You may hold your leg with your right
hand for support. Your toes should be pointed and
ankle tightened.

This exercise may be
executed while wearing light
ankle weights; but in the beginning,
exercise without them. Once you are
comfortable with the movements, you can
start with 2 pound ankle weights and work your
way up as your strength and flexibility permits.

Step 3
Slowly swing your leg upwards in a hinging motion. Exhale as you extend the leg.

Step 4
Draw the right leg back down as you prepare your return to the starting position. Inhale deeply.

Step 5
Return your right leg to the starting position.

Step 6
In this position, gently twist your torso towards the right knee, feeling the stretch across your back. Exhale. Repeat this exercise 10 times with each leg.

π *increases agility*

π *strengthens and stretches leg muscles*

Peacock Fly
Arm/Leg Fly

This exercise loosens and strengthens the inner thigh muscles, improves leg flexibility, and builds up the pectoral and lower abdominal muscles. You'll need a mat, a set of dumbbells, and a pair of ankle weights. Use light ankle weights and dumbbells in the beginning and increase the poundage as your strength improves. Even if you're in reasonably good shape, do this exercise slowly - concentrate on form.

Peacock Fly Challenge

For a more challenging approach to this exercise, you may wish to raise the arms at a 45 degree angle instead of 90 degrees. This variation works different portions of the chest muscles. If you raise your arms higher than shoulder level, be sure to use very light weights in order to avoid injury.

Step 1
Sit on the floor, holding dumbbells in each hand. Raise your knees, keeping your heels together.

Step 2
Inhale deeply. Tense your abdominal muscles. Round your back and slowly roll backwards, one vertebra at a time.

Step 3
Continue your descent as you slowly roll to the floor. Your arms naturally follow.

Step 4
Drop down to the floor with your arms at a 90 degree angle. Exhale. Arch your back. Inhale.

Step 5
Tense your abdominals. Now close your arms and legs back into the starting position. Exhale deeply. Perform 10 repetitions.

π *strengthens inner thighs*   π *improves leg flexibility*   π *builds pecs and abs*

Peacock Fly

Keep back as straight as possible.

Tighten abs and hold firm.

Arch back as you stretch.

The Art & Science
of the Calasanz System

The Calasanz System is a scientific approach to martial arts training that adds the discoveries of modern athletic science to the ancient knowledge of the masters. The techniques and conditioning exercises that make up the System train the body through isometric isolation that over time, produces a strong and supple physique.

Endurance training in this System is not fast paced, even though it can yield dramatic results in a short period of time. The System asks that a student train intelligently and consistently. A steadily paced training program allows adequate recuperation time for muscle groups, which helps students slowly build their bodies so they are able to handle the most rigorous training schedule without serious injury.

Avoiding Burnout

One of the biggest problems in any rigorous exercise regimen is student burnout. Ever since Calasanz opened his doors for business twenty years ago, it has been his mission to put students through a challenging workout that is also a satisfying one. In order to avoid student burnout, Calasanz tailors each student's goals individually; varying the course of study keeps the energy and enthusiasm at a very high level.

Take a Break

Calasanz believes that it's essential to take an occasional break from training. A week or two of rest, when needed, will rejuvenate you. Those committed to the martial arts find that after a break, they return excited and ready for new challenges.

Weekly Schedule

Calasanz recommends that you perform the exercises in this workbook no more than two days per week. On the third day of training, he advises students to practice basic martial arts techniques, learn kata, work on the wooden dummy or do Tai Chi or Wing Chun. If you are training at home, you may wish to choose another physical activity you enjoy for your third day of training.

Time of Training

We all have different body rhythms that dictate our energy levels throughout the day. And energy levels change as our bodies age and lifestyles alter. Switching training times is an effective method for bringing energy back to an optimal level.

Mental Motivation

Students appreciate the intellectual aspects of the martial arts, particularly after they've been training for some time. And one can rejuvenate interest in training during a period of physical burnout by pursuing the academic side of the martial arts. Reading books on martial arts philosophy such as *The Tao of Jeet Kune Do* by Bruce Lee can jump-start renewed interest. Martial arts movies can also help inspire you to get back to training.

Consider Martial Arts as a lifetime journey and commitment - and create a training schedule that's comfortably integrated into your overall lifestyle.

The Psychological Stages of Martial Arts Training

1. Uncertainty and insecurity
A true teacher leads the beginning student from fear and frustration into hopeful achievement.

2. Emptiness begins to fill
A sense of pride and physical well-being is generated by new skills. The student begins to ask the right questions.

3. Commitment
The realization dawns that true commitment is necessary. The mind and heart expand toward that goal.

4. Inner conflict
To attain mastery over the body and mind is a formidable task. Courage is tested. Some fall by the wayside. Others commit to going the distance.

5. The path to understanding
Those who have persevered, make a mighty breakthrough at this stage. They dedicate themselves to excellence.

6. Confidence and ability expand
Confidence and ability increase. Speed and power intensify. Knowledge is shared with those who know less.

7. High standards prevail
Ego gives way to a seasoned Martial Artist - one who understands The Way of the Peaceful Warrior.

8. The Inner Self is at one with the art
Respectful of others, grateful to his teachers, setting an example for those who come after him ... a true Martial Artist in body, mind and spirit, takes his place in the world he dreamed of entering.

"While the acquisition of belts is the outer symbol of growth towards Martial Arts mastery, the true challenge lies within."

THE BASIC BAR EXERCISES

The bar exercises on the following pages constitute your next step towards physical mastery in the Calasanz System ... and an introduction to applying your new knowledge in the practice of Martial Arts.

Flexing Horse Stretch
Horse and Front Stance Strengthener

This exercise requires you to shift from the front stance,
to the horse stance, and back to the front stance.
This process not only strengthens your legs
and trims your waistline; it provides
a firm grounding for many
fighting stances.

Step 1
Stand with the right side of your
body facing the bar. You should
be standing in front of the bar at
a 90 degree angle - with feet
together. While remaining in this
position, slightly twist your body
to the right and grasp the bar
with both hands. Your hands
should be a little more than
shoulder width apart.

Step 2
As you inhale deeply, lift yourself up onto the balls of your
feet.

Step 3
Lift your right knee to your chest
and grasp your leg with your left
hand. Flex your right foot.

π develops balance and poise

π strengthens legs

Step 4
Flex your foot again by pointing your toes
downward.

Step 5
Drop your torso forward as you grasp the
bar with your left hand. Your left supporting
leg should return to a flat footed position as
you simultaneously extend your right leg as
far back as comfortably possible.

Step 6
Exhale deeply as you extend the right leg
backwards. Inhale.

Flexing Horse Stretch

Step 7

Now drop your right leg as you step back into a narrow front stance and exhale. Make sure that your right leg is extended as far back as comfortably possible and that your right knee is straight. Your left leg is bent.

Step 8

The next step requires you to shift into a horse stance. Inhale. From your front stance, twist to the left until you are facing the bar and your weight is equally distributed between your left leg and your right leg. Your knees should be bent, your back straight and your feet pointed outward - parallel to the bar. Exhale upon completion of the horse stance.

From this position, inhale and twist to the left as you drop into a front stance. Exhale. Your left leg should now be extended and your right leg bent.

Step 10
Now bring your left leg forward, as you go back to the starting position. Your left side is now facing the bar and your feet should be together. Repeat this exercise 10 times as you alternate from right left, left to right, and so on

Flexing Horse Stretch

Keep body straight and parallel to bar as you
prepare to project leg up and back.

If you are unable to raise yourself on
the balls of your feet, omit this portion
of the exercise and just inhale deeply.

Point toes outward.
Torso should be parallel to the bar.

Grasping The Wind
Rib Cage & Torso Stretch

This exercise stretches the rib cage and the torso, and develops balance and leg strength. You should feel this stretch from head to toe. As you progress with these movements, you may choose to perform this exercise while holding a 1 to 2 pound dumbbell. Heavier weights should be avoided as they may cause injury to the arms and shoulders.

Step 1
Stand facing the bar and grasp the rail with both hands. Your hands should be a little more than shoulder width apart. Your feet should be firmly planted on the floor and parallel with your shoulders. Your back should be straight and chest out.

Step 2
Raise your body by slowly standing on balls of your feet. As you raise yourself upward, inhale deeply. If you are unable to raise yourself on the balls of your feet, omit this portion of the exercise and just inhale deeply.

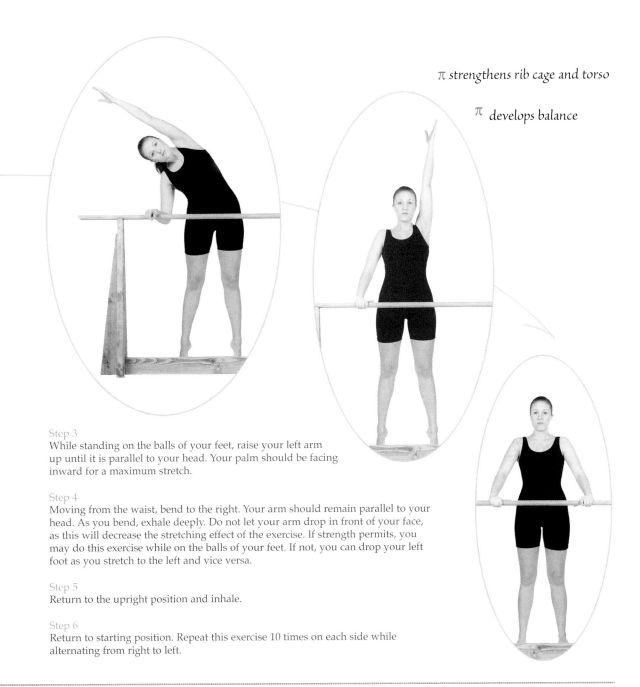

π *strengthens rib cage and torso*

π *develops balance*

Step 3
While standing on the balls of your feet, raise your left arm
up until it is parallel to your head. Your palm should be facing
inward for a maximum stretch.

Step 4
Moving from the waist, bend to the right. Your arm should remain parallel to your
head. As you bend, exhale deeply. Do not let your arm drop in front of your face,
as this will decrease the stretching effect of the exercise. If strength permits, you
may do this exercise while on the balls of your feet. If not, you can drop your left
foot as you stretch to the left and vice versa.

Step 5
Return to the upright position and inhale.

Step 6
Return to starting position. Repeat this exercise 10 times on each side while
alternating from right to left.

Grasping The Wind

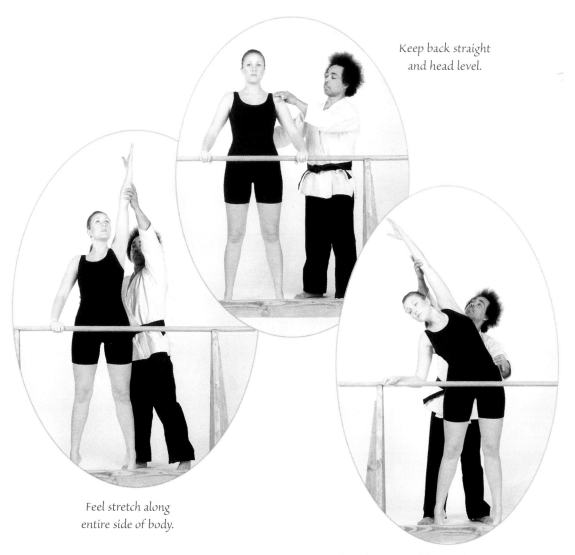

Keep back straight
and head level.

Feel stretch along
entire side of body.

Feel as if you are adding inches to your height.

Swinging Monkey
Swinging Split

Nothing is more impressive than seeing a
person drop into a full Japanese split.
The Swinging Monkey helps improve
the flexibility of your inner thigh
muscles which eventually result
in a deeper split and higher
kicks. It also helps firm the
gluteus maximus, a critical
muscle for executing
the side kick.

Step 1
Stand facing the bar and grasp the
rail with both hands. Your hands
should be a little more than shoulder
width apart. Your feet should be
firmly planted on the floor and parallel with your shoulders. Your back
should be straight and chest out.
Inhale deeply.

You may also choose to wear ankle weights.
Start with a light weight and increase your
poundage as your strength permits.

Step 2

While still holding the bar, slide your hands to the right. At the same time, simultaneously drop your torso to the right and raise your left leg. Raise the leg as high as comfortably possible. Concentrate on proper form and increase your height as your flexibility improves. Be sure to keep the torso and leg aligned and keep a straight posture. The foot of your kicking leg should be tensed and pointed toward the floor. The supporting leg should be straight with the foot pointed forward. Exhale deeply as the leg is raised.

Step 3

Return to the starting position. Inhale.

Step 4

Perform the exercise with the right leg. Alternate for 10 repetitions.

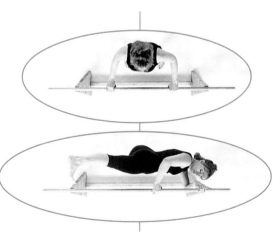

π *strengthens and stretches inner thighs for better splits*

Swinging Monkey

Approach the bar with correct posture and symmetry.

Swinging Monkey Variation

In Step 2 , the supporting leg is straight with the foot pointing forward. This position allows you to work the inner thigh muscles. A variation of this exercise emphasizes the gluteus maximus muscles. Instead of pointing the foot forward throughout the entire exercise, pivot the foot in the opposite direction of the kick. So if you are kicking with your right leg, pivot your left foot to the left and bend your left knee slightly.

White Tiger Stretch
Front Stance Enhancer

This exercise is designed to stretch the hamstring, strength-
en the supporting leg, and develop balance, poise and a
beautifully extended stance. The White Tiger
Stretch will introduce you to one of
karate's most basic stances -
Zenkutzo-Dachi, commonly
referred to as the
front stance.

Step 1

Face the bar and grasp the rail with
both hands. Hands should be a little
more than shoulder width apart; feet
should be firmly planted on the floor
and parallel with your shoulders;
back should be straight and chest out.

Step 2

Raise your body by slowly standing
on balls of your feet. As you raise
yourself upward, inhale deeply.

π develops balance and poise

π stretches hamstrings

Step 3
Lift your left knee as high as you can in a 45 degree angle and grasp your left leg with your left hand. If your strength permits, remain on the ball of your left foot. Pull your left leg as close to your chest as possible. Flex your left foot.

Step 4
Point your toes downward and tighten your ankle.

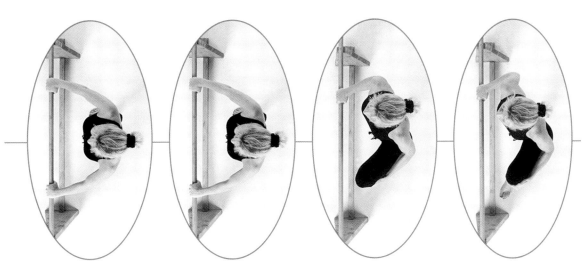

White Tiger Stretch

Step 5

Raise your left leg so it's parallel to the floor.

Step 6

Reach backwards with your left leg as far as you can, and exhale deeply.

Step 7

Now step backwards with your left leg. Both feet should be flat on the floor. Your left knee should be locked and extended as far as you comfortably can in order to get a good hamstring stretch. Your right leg should be bent. Sink as low as you can into this stance; torso facing forward and back straight. Avoid arching your back, as this may lead to lower back strain. Do 10 repetitions on each leg.

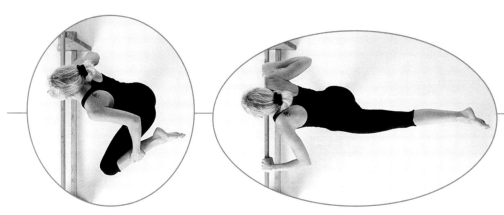

π prepares front stance muscles

π strengthens legs

π extends stretch

White Tiger Stretch

Keep back straight;
not arched.

Your left knee should be locked
and extended as far as you comfortably can in order to get a
good hamstring stretch.

Hold leg close to the body
to prepare for backward stretch.

Kick The Moon
Free The Chi
Swinging Cross and Front Raise Kick

Swinging Cross kicks and Front Raise kicks are as popular in the martial arts as are plies in ballet. These fundamental kicks, done over time, help stretch the hamstrings and add height to the kick.

π strengthens kick

π stretches hamstrings

Step 1
Stand with the left side of your body facing the bar. You should be standing in front of the bar at a 90 degree angle. Your feet should be together.

Step 2
Inhale and with control, swing your right leg as high as you can in line with the right shoulder. *Note: Your kicking foot should be tightly flexed during each kick.* Exhale at the pinnacle of your kick.

Step 3
Return to the starting position, with feet together.

Step 4
Inhale and with control, swing your right leg as high as you can towards the left shoulder. Exhale at the pinnacle of your kick then return to the starting position. Repeat this exercise 10 times with each leg.

Kick The Moon
Free The Chi

This exercise not only strengthens and stretches your legs; it encourages chi to flow freely through your system's meridiens.

Warrior Pivot
Low Swinging Roundhouse Kick

In this exercise, you simulate striking an opponent with a roundhouse kick to the shin and then to the head or midsection. This exercise introduces you to the Calasanz System Fighting Stance. To perform this stance, stand facing a mirror. Drop your right leg back so that the left side of your body is facing the mirror. Turn your head towards the mirror and raise your hands in front of your face and protect. Your weight is on your right leg and your left leg should lightly touch the floor. This stance may also be done with your right leg forward.

A fighter takes a stance which accommodates delivery of her strongest punch. A right handed puncher, for example, takes a stance with the left foot forward so that the right hand punch can be delivered with maximum torque.

Step 1
Standing at a comfortable distance from the bar, assume the Calasanz Fighting Stance with left foot forward.

Step 2
Drop your torso slightly backwards.

Step 3
Step slightly to the left with your left leg as you grab the bar. Inhale.

Step 4
Raise your right leg parallel to the floor, with knee bent.

π develops fighting stance

π strengthens roundhouse
    kick

Warrior Pivot

Step 5
Deliver a low roundhouse kick to your imaginary opponent's shin. Exhale

Steps 6, 7 & 8
Return to the starting position. Do 10 kicks per leg.

π develops pelvic strength

π adds power to kicks

Warrior Pivot

Maintain straight line of body.

Torque leg back for maximum thrust.

Aim kick to your imaginary opponent's vulnerable shin or knee.

Warrior Pivot II
High Swinging Roundhouse Kick

Step 1
Standing at a comfortable distance from the bar, assume the Calasanz Fighting Stance with left foot forward. Drop your torso slightly backwards.

Step 2
Step slightly to the left with your left leg as you grab the bar. Inhale.

Step 3
Raise your right leg parallel to the floor, with knee bent.

π develops balance and timing

π strengthens legs

Step 4
Deliver a high roundhouse kick to your imaginary opponent's midsection or head, depending on your flexibility. Exhale.

Steps 5 & 6
Return to the starting position. Do 10 kicks per leg.

Warrior Pivot II

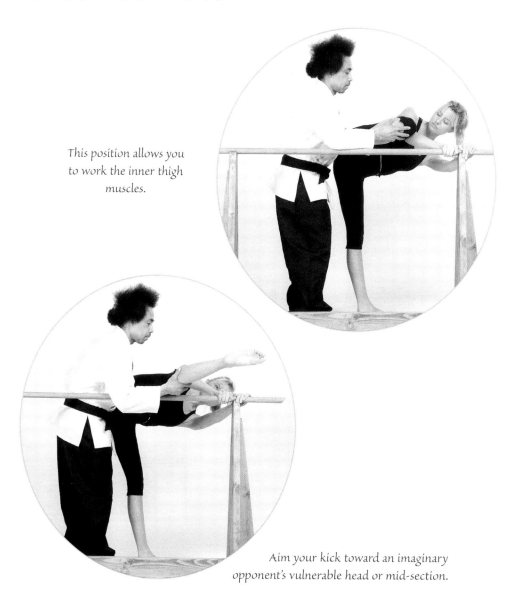

This position allows you to work the inner thigh muscles.

Aim your kick toward an imaginary opponent's vulnerable head or mid-section.

To do battle without knowledge

... is like trying to grasp the wind

When the Body is Ready
The Journey Unfolds

Now that your body is conditioned
and your mind is focused ... where does the path lead?

The purpose of the exercises on the preceding pages has been to create,
not only the body you've aspired to, but also a body that's capable of
following the path of the Warrior ... the path to Martial Arts mastery.

Two routes will have opened to you because of the work you've done in
re-creating your body: Karate and Kung Fu. These two ancient Warrior systems
derive from the same source: The journey of Bodhidharma to the Monastery at
Shaolin. It's important that you know something of the unique history of Martial
Arts, so you can understand that the body is only the beginning ... the next
level of mastery is that of the mind, heart and soul.

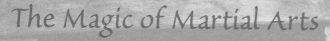

The Magic of Martial Arts

Martial Arts began so very long ago in China that the true origin of this remarkable fighting and healing discipline is shrouded in legend and fable. The most commonly accepted tale tells us that 1500 years ago, a Buddhist monk named Bodhidharma, traveled from India into China with the intention of finding his spiritual home.

Against implausible odds, he crossed the Himalayas, and finally came to rest at a hidden monastery called Shaolin. There, it seems, his spirit felt it had found a home among the nuns and monks who toiled at this hidden retreat, the name of which translates as "Young Forest."

It was at Shaolin that Bodhidharma founded the spiritual path that later came to be known as Zen Buddhism. Here, too, he created a system of exercises intended to make the monks he taught as strong in body as they were in mind and spirit.

The Way of the Universe

Years later, Shaolin would eventually become the Mecca of all Martial Arts . . . a training center destined to be the stuff of legend. All we truly know of it is this: If a Martial Artist aspired to train there, he could receive the greatest training for body, mind and spirit ever devised on this planet. But there was one rather daunting proviso to being accepted at the monastery: a student could leave Shaolin whenever he felt his training was complete - but he had to fight his way out. And all fights were to the death.

In the beginning, of course, the rarified art form that later became Kung Fu, Karate, Tai Chi, Chi Gung and a host of other styles we now know, so well, was merely a series of exercises. Special hand movements, body positions, breathing exercises and self-defense maneuvers were developed by Bodhidharma to allow his monks to meditate and exercise simultaneously. These maneuvers were also meant to teach them patience, courage, endurance and sensitivity, but at first, they simply seemed a curious collection of poses named for the animals and birds whose movements they echoed.

Evolution of Body and Spirit

The Horse Stance, for example, which resembles a man sitting on a horse, was the first of Bodhidharma's inventions. The monks and nuns were told to practice this difficult position for longer and longer periods of time each day; a feat more demanding than it seemed at first glance. By doing this, the monks learned balance and developed incredibly strong legs ... they became rooted or grounded, so that they could not be easily knocked over. Yet, there was much more in the Master's mind than simple body mastery when he conceived this Horse Stance. He admonished the monks to concentrate ... to focus on one thought alone, never moving to scratch or twitch or to relieve a cramp. He taught them to use their minds to conquer pain: to develop intensive focusing ability ... even to reach out with a "sixth sense" to anticipate attack.

The fighting system thus begun at Shaolin, continued to evolve over the years, as new approaches were created through trial and error, refining the Kung Fu knowledge to the sophisticated systems we know today. Kung Fu is actually a Western term - the Chinese called their fighting arts Wu Su (Woo Shoo).

Because the Shaolin fighters were nuns and monks, alongside their warrior skills they developed a strict moral code. Loyalty, respect, honor were the hallmarks of the Way of the Warrior. Unselfishness and benevolence were valued. The philosophy of Shaolin, which spread like wildfire throughout Asia, was not just meant to defeat one's enemies. It was meant to create of the self, an Enlightened Being.

Goju Ryu Karate

Goju Ryu Karate, which is the Karate style taught by Calasanz, is called an Okinawan style, for it's birthplace was the island of Okinawa, located between Japan and China.

In 1609, when the Japanese invaded Okinawa, all military action was banned and all weapons were confiscated from the Okinawans in order to prevent rebellion. In retaliation to this tyranny, the old Martial Arts monks in the mountains created a new system of Martial Arts. It involved toughening the hands, fingers, knuckles and elbows on straw pads and tree trunks ... adding flying leaps to unseat the enemy on horseback ... changing staves and bows and agricultural implements into weapons. Within a short time, the formidable skills of "open-hand" karate had been perfected.

The transformation of oppressed farmers into a deadly fighting machine was the birth of "the way of the empty hand" ... now known throughout the world as karate.

Wing Chun Kung Fu

Wing Chun is the Kung Fu form taught in the Calasanz System. This is a fighting form that has an intriguing and illustrious history. Two hundred eighty years ago, China was ruled by the repressive Manchus, who outlawed all weapons and forbade the Hans (comprising 90% of the population) to practice any form of self-defense. The Hans began to train a secret army of revolutionaries. The Sil Lim Temple became the sanctuary where masters of many ancient Martial Arts systems deliberated on how to create a single style that would be deadly enough to serve their revolutionary purpose, but which could be taught faster than the traditional form that took 20 years to master. Five of China's greatest grandmasters jointly created a new system, but before they could teach it to their secret army, the Manchus burned the temple and put the Masters to death.

Preserving the Secrets

Ng Mui, a nun, was the only survivor of the original Grandmasters group. In secret, and in great danger, she taught the system to a talented young orphan girl whom she named Wing Chun, which means "hope for the future." The lineage and secrets of this extraordinary system were closely guarded for two and a half centuries. The Wing Chun system equalizes the height and weight advantage that men have over women because it brings combat in closer to the opponent's body, where the length of arms and legs no longer determine advantage.

Bruce Lee, a brilliant practitioner of Wing Chun,
shared his knowledge with the West - many believe he signed his
own death warrant by doing so, as the powerful old Masters in China
wished to keep the secrets in Asia. This remarkable Kung Fu form is
studied at Calasanz as part of the System's curriculum.

The Path
Through The Portal

Calasanz invites you to step into the world of Martial Arts,
with certainty that whatever you seek there, can be yours. Physical fitness,
mental discipline, focus, enhanced energy ... all are part of the transformation
to be experienced on the journey to Martial Arts Mastery.

To study the Calasanz System
is to step through a Portal
to a new life of your
own choosing.

The way

... is in training

Musashi

Dedication

I wish to dedicate this book to my students, whom I consider
both friends and allies on life's path. It is a great pleasure to share this
extraordinary journey with you.

Acknowledgement

There are certain students who, over the years, have participated in the evolution of my
system and my life with unwavering belief and loyalty. I wish to acknowledge both their
contribution and friendship: Beth Arthur, Jim Briggs, Cathy Cash, Tony Esposito, Dennis
Grimaldi, Edith Harris, Grace A. Luppino, Dave Tartaglia and Dolly Williams.
And very special thanks to Grace Luppino for her meticulous and
eloquent descriptions of the Calasanz System exercises.

 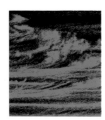  

Disclaimer